Besa La Mano
Embracing Respect and Heritage

First Edition

ISBN: 979-8-9890864-9-8

This book is self-published by Jasdomin Santana
Contact: jasdomin@outlook.com

This is a work of fiction. Names, characters, businesses, places, events, locales, and incidents are either the products of the author's imagination or used in a fictitious manner. Any resemblance to actual persons, living or dead, or actual events is purely coincidental.

Printed in the United States of America

On a sunny Sunday, Luis, a happy boy from New York, plays baseball with friends, laughing and having fun.

1

After the game, Luis's parents tell him about a special trip to the Dominican Republic, showing him exciting pictures.

They talk about "besando la mano," a way to show respect and love, especially to family.

Luis tries "besando la mano" with his stuffed animals, imagining they are his family in the Dominican Republic.

Packing their bags, Luis and his family are super excited, thinking about the adventures ahead.

They hop on a plane, waving goodbye. Luis peeks out the window, eager for what is to come.

When the plane lands, everyone claps! Luis is surprised - he did not know about this fun tradition.

Stepping into the warm, sunny Dominican Republic, they are greeted by music and palm trees dancing in the wind.

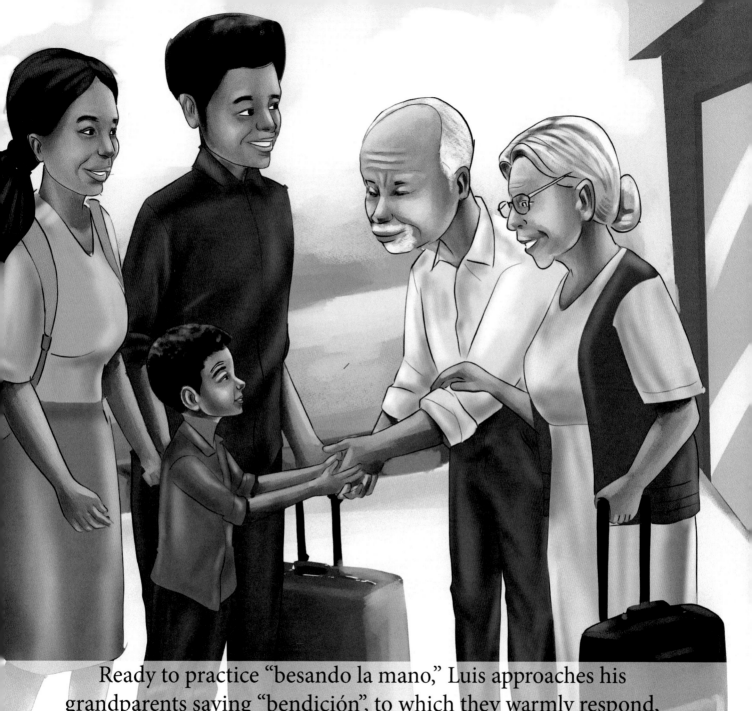

Ready to practice "besando la mano," Luis approaches his
grandparents saying "bendición", to which they warmly respond,
"Que Dios te bendiga."

His grandparents hug him tight, saying, "Pero que grande estas!" Luis feels their love and happiness.

Driving through the busy streets, Luis gazes at the colorful scenes
and lively markets.

11

Luis explores the lively markets, amazed by all the colors, crafts, and friendly faces.

12

In the kitchen, Luis watches Abuela make Sancocho. "Can you fetch an avocado from el colmado?" she asks.

13

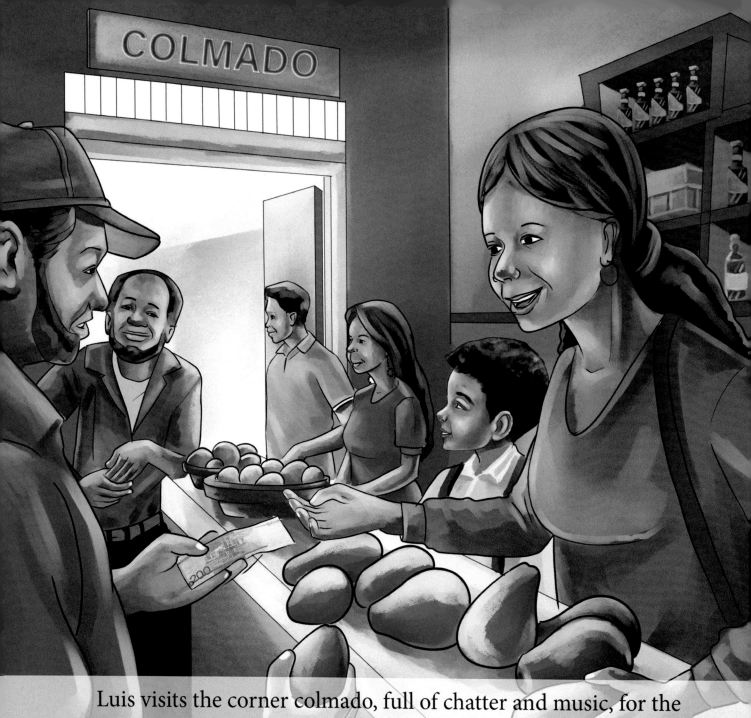

Luis visits the corner colmado, full of chatter and music, for the avocado.

Talking in Spanish, Luis buys an avocado, proud of himself for helping Abuela.

At dinner, the Sancocho is so yummy that Luis asks for more, his belly happy.

16

That night on the porch, Abuela tells Luis about El Galipote, a mysterious creature that can change shape and is known for its magical, secretive ways in the night. Luis listens, wide-eyed, imagining such mysterious adventures.

In bed, Luis dreams of El Galipote and other legends, feeling like a hero in these stories.

18

The next day, Luis and his mom go swimming in a beautiful river in "el campo," surrounded by green trees.

Luis picks fruits and rides a donkey, laughing with joy.

At a family gathering, Luis greets everyone by "besando la mano," feeling proud and connected.

21

Surrounded by his family, Luis feels a special connection to his Dominican roots.

Saying goodbye, they promise to see each other again during Semana Santa. Luis feels a mix of sadness and excitement, already dreaming of his next visit.

Back home, Luis tells his friends all about his trip and the special tradition of "besando la mano."

24